# CHEMISTRY: First S-T-E-P-S

CHEMISTRY
First S-T-E-P-S

by Keith Gordon Irwin

illustrated by Julio Granda

FRANKLIN WATTS, INC.
575 Lexington Ave. · New York 22

Contents

CHEMISTRY: First S-T-E-P-S

1

The Magic of Chemistry

THE SCIENCE of chemistry studies and explains the *changes* that substances undergo. These changes can seem like magic. And they are magic — *chemical magic*. In such a change an old substance disappears and suddenly a new substance takes its place. For example, when a birthday candle is lighted, the material out of which the candle is made disappears as a gas that rises toward the ceiling. That is a chemical change. A piece of steel wool left in a damp place changes to soft, red-brown rust — a very different substance from the original steel wool. That, too, is a chemical change. Berries in the garden that are, as yet, unripe will soon lose their sourness and become tasty and sweet. Again, the change is a chemical one.

Sometimes chemical magic is useful, but often it is not. If someone at your house, for example, put sugar into a dry pan, started to heat it on the stove, and then forgot about it, we can guess what would happen. By the time that person hurried back and snatched the pan from the burner there would be only a black mass where the sugar had been. This kind of chemical magic is something that is not wanted in candy making.

1

sugar

sugar with water

On the other hand, if the sugar with some liquid added is heated as it should be to make caramel candy, the color would become light brown and something would be produced with a pleasant odor and a delightful taste. This time, the chemical magic would be quite to our liking.

Actually, the cooking of food is *filled* with chemical magic. Think for a moment of the delicious odors coming from a bakery shop. Or meat roasting in the oven. The dough of rolls and cakes never smelled like that before they were baked; the meat never smelled as good before roasting. The chemical changes made by the fire have produced new substances from old. That is chemical magic.

✦2

Reading Messages by Chemical Magic

IF YOU like to experiment, you can use a chemical change to bring out secret messages. Take an empty piepan of thin aluminum and cut a sheet of ordinary writing paper to fit it. With a small water-color brush and the juice of a lemon make secret marks or words on the paper. Set the pan and paper in a warm place to let the writing dry. That is the first part of the experiment.

Now take the paper out. In its place put a candle in the pan, using some drops of melted paraffin or wax from the candle to hold the candle upright. Light the candle and hold the paper above the flame, moving it around so that the heat turns the lemon juice a dark color. The dark effect does not disappear when the paper is taken away from the flame. As you will see, a chemical change has made the message easy to read.

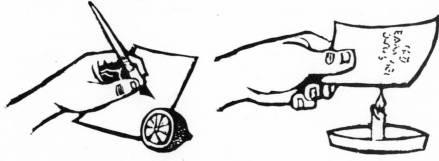

3

The Chemical Story of Rust

Some chemical changes do not require heat. For example, if a wad of clean steel wool is left in a damp place, it will change to red-brown rust. No heat has to be applied in this chemical change, in which one substance has vanished and another has appeared.

One might suppose that such a chemical change as this is easily explained. One might say, "Isn't the iron still there, hidden under a reddish-brown coating?" To find out, simply hold a magnet over the rust. While iron and steel are strongly attracted to a magnet, rust is not. You find there is no pull at all. The iron is *not* still there under a red-brown cloak.

If you have access to a good balance or scale, weigh the rust. You find that it is heavier than the steel wool had been. Where did the extra weight come from? The answer is: the extra weight came from the *oxygen* in the air.

But, you might object that oxygen is a gas and iron is a solid. How could they, together, form the reddish-brown rust? That is something that neither Benjamin Franklin nor George Washington could have explained. Today, we can find the answer in any book

4

on chemistry. An iron nail or steel wool is made up of *iron atoms.* In the metal itself, these atoms are close together and pull strongly upon each other, making the metal strong and hard. The oxygen particles in the air are made up of *oxygen atoms.* These atoms have only a slight attraction for each other, so oxygen is not strong at all. It is a gas. In rust, two iron atoms and three oxygen atoms combine to form an atom group, or cluster. The rust itself is made of millions of these clusters, all just alike. Each cluster is pulled upon by all the nearby clusters. But this pull is much less than that between the iron atoms in iron and steel, though more than the slight pull between the oxygen atoms in the air particles. Thus, rust is a solid — but a weak solid that falls easily into powdery dust.

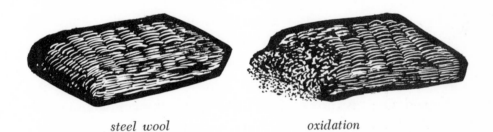

steel wool   oxidation

Don't bother getting out your microscope to prove these points. Atoms are unbelievably tiny. You will see rust particles with your microscope, all right, but you will not be able to see the separate atoms in the rust. Most certainly you will not be able to count the number of iron and oxygen atoms in each group or cluster. How then, you might be asking yourself, can we talk about atoms and how they behave in some chemical change when we cannot even see them or follow them with our eyes. Actually, the *mind* has to follow what the eye cannot see. That is a very important point to remember when trying to understand what happens in chemistry.

4

Thinking About Atoms

THERE ARE more than a hundred kinds of atoms out of which the earth and all of the things in it have been made. Some substances, like iron, are formed from a single kind of atom. These are known as *elements*, and are listed in the Table of Elements on page 44. There are, in nature, several hundred substances whose atom groups or clusters are made of two kinds of atoms. Rust is an example, and so is water. Several thousand substances have more than two kinds of atoms. There is a name given to any substance whose atom group or cluster has more than one kind of atom. It is called a *compound*.

Another name for an atom group or cluster is *molecule*. Molecules should be thought of as independent little particles. In the case of compounds, the molecules will always have two or more kinds of atoms packed together. Water molecules, for example, contain two hydrogen atoms and one oxygen atom. The chemist indicates the molecular make-up by writing the *formula* for the water molecule, in one of the following four ways —

6

$$\text{HHO,} \quad \text{HOH,} \quad \begin{array}{c} \text{H} \\ \text{O,} \\ \text{H} \end{array} \text{or} \quad \text{H}_2\text{O.}$$

The last form is the one that is usually used. In such a formula, H represents a hydrogen atom, O the oxygen atom.

The molecule of sugar is quite complex in its make-up. It has a total of 45 atoms. Of these, 12 are carbon atoms, 22 are hydrogen atoms, and 11 are oxygen atoms. Using the letters C, H and O for the three kinds of atoms the formula for sugar would look like this, provided the atoms were lined up:

CCCCCCCCCCCCHHHHHHHHHHHHHHHHHHHHHHOOOOOOOOOOO.

Usually, however, the formula is put down in a compact way like this: $C_{12}H_{22}O_{11}$. Although not shown by the formula, the 12 carbon atoms are like beads strung together, while the other atoms are hooked onto the carbon atoms.

Now, at the center of the string of carbon atoms is a weak point. When heated with a small amount of liquid, the big sugar molecule splits at this weak point. The products of this chemical change are *glucose* and *fructose*, both of which are kinds of sugars. (Fructose is sweeter than glucose. Though both are formed in nature, fructose is the kind of sugar that is abundant in honey, raisins and dates.) These sugars have the same formula, which means that their molecules are built from the same number and kinds of atoms. But the atoms are not *packed* in the same way.

7

To keep track of the shifts of atoms in the chemical change of sugar to glucose and fructose, the chemist writes what he calls an *equation*. Since one molecule of water was used up in the action it has to be included.

$$C_{12}H_{22}O_{11} + \text{strong heat} \longrightarrow 12\,C + 11\,H_2O.$$
$$\text{(sugar)} \qquad\qquad\qquad \text{(equals)} \ \text{(carbon)} \ \text{(water)}$$

You might like to see another equation. This one is for the chemical change that occurs when dry sugar is heated strongly. The black mass that is formed is carbon; the puffs of steam that appear show that water is being formed in the action. The equation makes clear that the big sugar molecule is being almost completely broken into fragments.

$$C_{12}H_{22}O_{11} + H_2O + \text{heat} \longrightarrow C_6H_{12}O_6 + C_6H_{12}O_6.$$
$$\text{(sugar)} \qquad \text{(water)} \qquad\quad \text{(equals)} \ \text{(glucose)} \quad \text{(fructose)}$$

✦5

Watching Atoms Change Places

IN SOME chemical changes, atoms of two different kinds exchange places. Let us perform an experiment in which iron atoms and copper atoms exchange places. You will not be able to *see* the atoms do this, but you will be certain *in your mind* that the exchange is taking place.

The experiment calls for about half a teaspoonful of blue vitriol crystals. First, put the crystals in a glass dish and pour over them about half a cup of hot water, stirring the mixture occasionally with a wooden stick. The crystals will dissolve slowly. At first the color will be light blue, then dark blue. For the experiments you will be making, the light blue solution will be best. When you are through, do not throw away any unused blue vitriol solution. Set it aside to let the water evaporate. Beautiful small crystals will appear. Put them into a vial or bottle and tighten the cap. Be sure to label the bottle Blue Vitriol.

9

Next, pour some of the blue solution into a small glass. Taking a clean nail in your hand, dip the lower part of it into the solution. Count slowly up to three, then take the nail out and dry it lightly on a piece of paper toweling. A red coating should be on the nail. This coating is copper — real copper!

Now put the nail back into the solution again and leave it there for a few minutes. See if you can tell from the surface roughness of the nail — on the part that has been in the liquid — whether some of the iron of the nail has been removed in the chemical change. This should be the case.

The action between the iron of the nail and the blue vitriol solution will be rather slow. It can take place only at the outer surface of the nail, for that is where the solution touches. The action is slow because the surface of a single nail is not large. To get a much faster action, put a small wad of clean steel wool into the same solution. The steel wool fibers are just like the nail in that they are made of iron. Almost instantly every little fiber will become red with copper.

You may not realize it at first but the color of the solution will also change when the steel wool is left in. The blue disappears and a pale green color forms. The new color is due to a new substance being formed. This is green vitriol. (Your solution may become muddy in appearance, with a rusty color near the surface, but that will be due to a separate chemical change produced by the oxygen in the air.)

We are now ready to work out an explanation as to what has taken place. First, we shall need to put the substances into a word-equation:

$$\text{Blue vitriol} + \text{iron} \longrightarrow \text{green vitriol} + \text{copper}$$

Since iron is listed among the elements in the table on page 44, it is composed of but one kind of atom — the atom of iron. Copper is also an element, so it is composed of but one kind of atom — the atom of copper. From the equation, we can be sure that the blue vitriol *must* contain copper atoms in its molecules, and green vitriol *must* contain iron atoms in its molecules. Therefore the iron atoms and copper atoms *must have exchanged places*. Of course, we did not see the atoms doing this for they were much too tiny, but *our minds* can be certain about it.

After finishing this experiment, you should do as every good chemist does. He washes all containers with *plenty of water*, and wipes up every drop of spilled liquid with paper toweling. If he did not do this, his chemicals might become contaminated, which would make his results incorrect.

✦6

What the Nose Knows

How INTERESTING it would be if we had a microscope so powerful that it would let us see the atoms as they build molecules. If we had such an instrument, we could, for example, see how a ripe pineapple puts the atoms together that give the very special substance we call "pineapple odor."

Simply by smelling a pineapple, your nose *knows* that an odorous substance is being formed which, most certainly, will keep on being formed as long as the fruit remains. And, as your nose also knows, no other plant but the one that grows pineapples can make this particular substance.

Chemistry text books say that the substance that gives the odor to the ripe pineapple is *methyl butyrate.* The formula is given as $CH_3 \cdot C_4H_7O_2$, the dot showing the point of connection between the methyl part (CH_3) and the butyrate part ($C_4H_7O_2$). It is an oil and evaporates readily.

Other kinds of fruit, too, have their own individual chemical odors. The peach makes *ethyl butyrate.* Its formula is given as $C_2H_5 \cdot C_4H_7O_2$, the second part of both formulas being the same. The main odor in apple cider is that of *amyl butyrate,* whose formula is given as $C_3H_7 \cdot C_4H_7O_2$. Again, the second part of the formula is the same as those of the others.

Chemists use the word *ester* for such odorous plant oils. There are many of them. The second part of an ester's formula does not, however, need to be a butyrate. Sometimes it is an *acetate*. For example, the ester of ripe bananas is *ethyl acetate*, while that of ripe oranges is *octyl acetate*. Sometimes it is a *salicylate*. The ester produced by the red berries of the wintergreen shrub is *methyl salicylate*. It is used as a food flavoring and for medical use under the name "oil of wintergreen."

Other plant parts beside the fruit and berries can form odorous esters, too. When you pinch a leaf of a geranium in the flower garden, the spicy fragrance of the geranium ester fills the air for a moment. When you crush some mint leaves in your hand you get the pleasant odor of peppermint. Across the fields you can perhaps smell the "odor of the pines," which is an ester produced by pine trees.

Chemists are able to duplicate many of these plant esters. They can, for example, make the one that the Mexican vanilla-bean produces by putting into their artificial product the same kinds of atoms, arranged in the same way. To keep the two from being confused, the plant product is called *vanilla*, while the chemist-made product is called *vanillin* or *artificial vanilla*. Look at the label on your kitchen vanilla bottle, or at the ones in the food stores and you can tell, from the wording, which product is used in the bottle.

✦7

The Chemist in the Berry Patch

LET US look in on the wonderful chemistry that is taking place in the berry patch. The fruit of the blackberries, loganberries, dewberries, and black raspberries are now starting to turn red. All of them seem to be using the same dye color for their fruit. The purple grape also uses it.

With all of *these* plants, *redness* of the fruit does not mean *ripeness*. It means *acid*. A red-colored berry is one that is *sour with acid*. You can check on this yourself. Start with some purple grape juice. To a sample of this liquid, add a small amount of acid. *Any* acid will do; use vinegar or lemon juice, for example. The color of the solution instantly becomes red. Only an acid will produce this color; thus we can be sure that the red-colored fruit contains acid.

As the fruit ripens, the acid is used up in a chemical way as the flavors and sugars of the fruit form. With the acid gone, the color changes to purple or purplish-black. You can try to get the purple color from the grape juice you made red with acid. Use an *anti-acid,* or *base,* a substance which neutralizes acids. Try a pinch of baking soda, a little borax, or even some soapy water. If you add *too much* anti-acid — which is very easy to do — the color will go

14

to purple and then on to blue. If you do happen to get this blue color, add a drop or so of acid and the color should change to purple. But be careful — if you add *too much* acid it will go on to red. Even after several trials you may still fail to get the purple color to stay. But the berry plant has no trouble at all in getting rid of even the tiniest trace of acid; its berries will be beautifully purple.

When the berries are ripe, the plant does something more. It produces a chemical substance that removes some of the cell walls in the fruit, making it soft. Also softened are most of the fibers holding the berry to the plant so, as we reach for it, the fruit almost drops into our hand. As we slip the berry into our mouth and taste its delicious flavor we can say, in all sincerity, "What a perfectly marvelous chemical accomplishment the making of a ripe berry is!"

Actually, one should not get the impression that red-colored fruit is *always* unripe fruit. An apple's redness that colors its skin where the sunshine strikes it is of a different chemical substance from that of the unripe berry or grape. No anti-acid will turn *it* blue. Nor is the red of the tomato and the red of the beet like the others.

15

8

Catching a Gas and Holding It

THE PLANT ester that we call "essence of Heliotrope" is a perfume and must be kept in a tight bottle or it will disappear. If the stopper is left off, the liquid changes to a colorless *vapor* which passes out of the bottle as molecules. We cannot *see* the molecules going out of the bottle neck, but our nose knows how far they have gone from the place where they started.

Water, when poured into a pan and left in a warm place, will soon evaporate and disappear as a colorless vapor. As its molecules move off they will mix with the colorless molecules of the air. But air itself is not a vapor. It is a *gas*. Like other gases, its molecules do not tend to cluster into drops, as those of liquids do, but stay scattered out.

The air that is all about us is really a mixture of several colorless gases. Oxygen makes up about a fifth and nitrogen most of the rest. Both of these gases are odorless, as well as colorless, so there is no way our nose or our eyes can pick them out or identify them. Chemical tests must be used to do that.

A candle flame can be used as a chemical test for the oxygen in the air. In this test, the oxygen will be removed and the nitrogen

16

left behind. Set a large candle in a pan by making a little mound of melted wax from the candle to hold it upright, as shown in the sketch. Fill the pan about three-fourths full of water. Over the burning candle lower an empty pickle jar with a wide mouth. With the mouth of the jar resting on the bottom of the pan, some bubbles will, at first, rise around the outside of the jar. Then the water will start to rise inside of the jar, as the oxygen in the air of the jar is used up. The flame will soon burn poorly, the water will stop rising, then the flame will go out. The oxygen is gone. Nitrogen is left.

BURNING THE OXYGEN OUT OF AIR

Another colorless, odorless gas is *carbon dioxide*. Two centuries ago, Jan Van Helmont, a Belgian scientist, made this gas in a chemical way by mixing soda and vinegar. Van Helmont noticed that bubbles of gas came off, but he did not know what the gas was. He was using a bottle and to prevent the gas bubbles from

17

escaping into the air, he corked the bottle tightly. As Van Helmont held the bottle in his hand and peered through the glass, the bottle suddenly burst and his face was cut by flying glass. More surprised than hurt, he wondered what the "wild, untamed spirit" was that forced its way out of the bottle.

JAN VAN HELMONT AND THE "WILD SPIRIT"

When Van Helmont sat down to write about his experiment, he decided that "spirit" was not the right word to use for "the thing" in the bottle. People might think he was talking about an elf or a fairy. So he made up a word — and that word has been used ever since. This is what Van Helmont wrote:

"This spirit, hitherto unknown, I call by a new name GAS, as something which cannot be confined in a vessel nor reduced to a body that can be seen."

18

Actually, Van Helmont could have prepared his gas safely if he had used a thick-walled bottle. In repeating his experiment *in a safe way,* put a heaping teaspoonful of baking soda into a clean pop bottle and pour in three or four times that much vinegar. Do not cork the bottle but press the dampened palm of your hand rather lightly against the bottle's mouth. The carbon dioxide which is forming should exert some pressure against your hand. Now add another spoonful of soda and more vinegar to that already in the pop bottle. This time press in a cork firmly and *stand back.* In a minute or so the pressure of the gas will be strong enough to pop the cork out of the bottle.

The gas you have formed — carbon dioxide — is heavier than air. You can prove this for yourself by using a yardstick, a pencil having six sides, and two good-sized paper cups which are just alike.

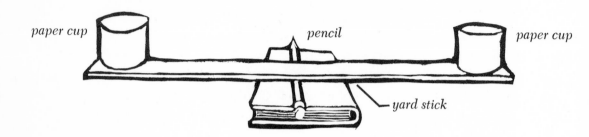

paper cup   pencil   paper cup

yard stick

Using a milk bottle with the soda and vinegar solution, as before, to collect some carbon dioxide for this experiment, place a thin book on a flat surface like a table, put the pencil on the book, and balance the yardstick at its center on the pencil. Now place the paper cups near the ends of the stick, with everything in balance. Out of the milk bottle pour the carbon dioxide *downward* into one of the paper cups. (Be careful not to pour in any vinegar.) That side of the "gas-balance" should suddenly go down, for the carbon dioxide in the cup will be heavier than the air in the other cup. (In less than ten minutes you may find that the balance will come back to a level position again. Why? Because the carbon dioxide has worked out of the cup into the air.)

Carbon dioxide will put out a flame if there is enough of it to push away the oxygen that permits the flame to burn. You can show this by putting a small candle in the bottom of a tall jar, lighting the candle, then pouring the carbon dioxide downward into the jar.

A good chemical test for carbon dioxide makes use of clear *limewater*. Get about four fluid ounces of it, so you will have the supply for several experiments.

carbon dioxide

Put about two tablespoonful of the limewater into a clean glass jar, then pour down into the jar some of the carbon dioxide you have made. Cover the mouth of the jar with the palm of your hand and shake the liquid and gas together. Thousands of fine white particles will form, which give the liquid a milky appearance. *No gas except carbon dioxide gives this milky appearance to limewater.* (Again, do not let any vinegar pour down with the carbon dioxide because it will spoil the test.)

There are a number of other experiments you can do with limewater, and all of them have to do with carbon dioxide. You can *prove* that your breath has carbon dioxide in it by taking a drinking straw and bubbling your breath into a sample of limewater. The liquid will turn milky. You can also *prove* that a burning candle gives off carbon dioxide by catching some of the gases that rise above the flame. Use a bottle *several inches above the flame* to catch the gases. Then close the mouth of the bottle for a moment as you set the bottle on the table. Now pour in some limewater and shake the liquid and gas together. Again, the liquid will turn milky.

✤9

A Chemical Adventure with George Washington

CARBON DIOXIDE is but one of several colorless, odorless gases. Another is methane (CH_4), or "marsh gas." The story of how it got the marsh-gas name is an interesting one in the history of chemistry.

John Dalton, an 18th century English chemist, thought that a gas which kept bubbling up through the swampy marsh near his home was probably carbon dioxide. One day he caught some in a bottle and tested it with limewater. No milkiness appeared. Carbon dioxide does not burn but this gas burned, giving off a pale bluish flame. Dalton called it "marsh gas," and wondered whether the strange pale light seen at night flitting across the marshes — people called it the will-o'-the-wisp — might not in fact be caused by the burning of the bubbling marsh gas. Later, he found out that it was.

Here we should say something more about the burning in Dalton's experiment. The gas gave no test for carbon dioxide *before* it was burned; however, there was a strong test for carbon dioxide *after* the burning. Where had the carbon dioxide come from? After much thinking, Dalton came up with the answer. The marsh gas must have furnished the carbon atoms; the air, the oxygen atoms for the carbon dioxide formed. When the gas was on fire a *cold* surface held above the flame became covered with a film of moisture. Where did the water of the moisture come from? Water, reasoned Dalton, is a compound made from hydrogen and oxygen atoms. Marsh gas had evidently supplied the hydrogen atoms, the air had supplied the oxygen atoms. Marsh gas, then, must be a compound of carbon and hydrogen atoms. Dalton put down its formula as HHCHH. Today, the same formula is usually written CH_4. The official chemical name for the gas is now *methane*.

When news of Dalton's experiments reached America, George Washington and a few of his friends immediately thought of the swampy places along the Potomac River where gas bubbles also rose to the water surface. They wondered whether this might not be the same as Dalton's marsh gas, and decided to find out. Taking a boat out to the marshy area of the Potomac, they located a place where many bubbles were rising. With them they had brought a pole made from a long branch which had a bottle tied to one end. The bottle was tied sideways, so could be filled while under water by twisting the pole. Full of water and with its mouth kept under water, the bottle was pushed to a place where the bubbles were rising. In this way, Washington and his companions succeeded in collecting the bubbling gas. When the bottle was full the pole was drawn to the boat and the bottle corked and removed from the pole. Other bottles were filled in the same way, after which the men went to the home of one of them to do their experimenting. When they were through they decided that their gas of the marshes was indeed the same substance as Dalton's marsh gas.

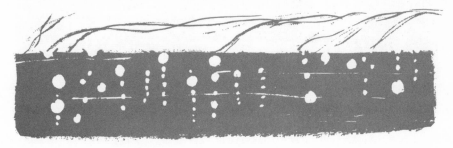

Here is a chemical problem for *you*. Using Dalton's methods, how would you go about proving that the paraffin or wax of a candle contains both carbon and hydrogen atoms? You will, of course, want to use the limewater test on the gases caught *above* the burning candle. There are two ways to get the film of moisture on a cold surface. Put a cold plate near the candle flame, as pictured. That is one way. Another way is to fill a pan with cold water, without getting any water on the outside. Then the pan should be held just above the flame. Drops of water should form and can be caught in a glass. (Your experiments, of course, will not give you the formula itself. All you will be able to say is that "the formula for paraffin is $C_x H_y$ in which the x and y are numbers.")

COLLECTING GAS IN THE MARSH ALONG THE POTOMAC RIVER

✤10

Heating with Marsh Gas

AT THIS POINT, you may be wondering why someone does not collect marsh gas from marshes and pipe it into houses to be used in ovens and stoves. Actually, this gas *is* being piped to houses — but the supply does not come from marshes. If gas is used in your home for heating or cooking, you might call the manager of the gas company and ask him whether the gas he sells is either largely or wholly methane. (Methane is the name he would use for marsh gas.) He should be glad to tell you, if you ask, where their supply comes from.

The type of gas burner used today in all school laboratories was invented a century ago by Robert Bunsen, a German chemist. Before Bunsen's burners came into use, the burning of gas as a fuel was considered very dangerous. Explosions had often occurred. Bunsen's burner was made entirely of metal, and was both safe and simple to operate. His first device is shown in the accompanying sketch. The gas, under a slight pressure, was made to pass out of a small opening. A metal tube, open at each end, fitted loosely over the gas opening. When the gas was turned on at the valve, the gas rushing into the metal tube caused air to be drawn in. The gas

25

THE BUNSEN BURNER (EARLY FORM)

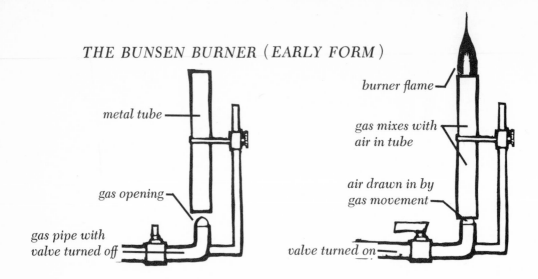

metal tube

gas opening

gas pipe with
valve turned off

burner flame

gas mixes with
air in tube

air drawn in by
gas movement

valve turned on

and air were then mixed in the metal tube. When the mixture was ignited at the top of the tube a hot, conical flame formed. If *too much* air was drawn in, the burning was noisy and the flame might easily go out. If *too little* air entered, the flame was weak and smoky. Accordingly, the tube could be moved up or down to make the air flow just right. In today's laboratory burner the air openings are merely changed in size.

If gas is used in your home the stove parts will match the basic *idea* of Bunsen's plan, although the actual form will be different. Examine the stove. The burner part is arranged to be removable. With it off, you will be able to see the small opening through which the gas passes when the valve is turned on. In the removed part you will find the tube where the gas and air mix, as well as the air openings that may be turned to let more air in, or less air in. Finally you will see the many small openings where the gas will burn when ignited.

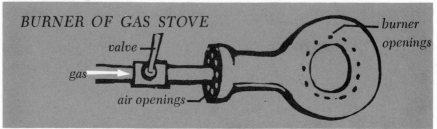

BURNER OF GAS STOVE

valve

gas

air openings

burner
openings

26

✦11

Happenings in a Wood Fire

THE BURNING of a log of wood is not as simple a chemical matter as the burning of methane in a Bunsen burner. A century and a half ago the chemical changes were shown by heating wood or sawdust in an old gunbarrel. Many substances formed — some as liquids, others as gases, while one was left in the gunbarrel as a solid. All of these substances will burn and, if the wood had been in an open fire, only a little ash and gases like carbon dioxide would have remained.

Among the substances formed in this experiment were wood tar, a dark sticky liquid; "wood vinegar," which is the same acid as that in cider vinegar; methanol, an important solvent; burnable "wood gases"; and wood charcoal. And *all of these things would have burned up if the wood had been in the fireplace.*

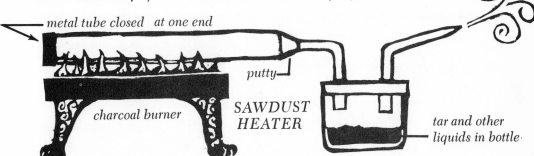

metal tube closed at one end

putty

charcoal burner   SAWDUST HEATER

tar and other liquids in bottle

27

✦12

Chemical Factories of the Fields

WITH CARBON DIOXIDE pouring out into the air from so many chimneys and with more added by the breathing of animals and people, did you ever wonder what was to keep the air from being so full of this gas that candle flames would go out and fires would die down? The reason this does not happen is that the plants take the carbon dioxide out of the air. What do they do with it? They use it as a mine for carbon atoms — atoms that they then build into wonderful carbon compounds.

Have you ever stood beside a field of sugar beets in early autumn? The roots of the beets are getting sweeter day by day from the sugar that the plants are forming out of carbon atoms that had been, only a short time before, in the carbon dioxide molecules of the air. But you will hear no sounds as the twelve carbon atoms of the sugar molecule drop into place, no noise as the 22 hydrogen and the 11 oxygen atoms are hooked on.

Perhaps a few miles away from the beet field is a large brick building with a tall chimney. There, when harvested, the beets will be cut into slices and the slices will be mixed with heated water to soak out the sugar. After that, the solution will be

28

treated to remove undesirable materials, then concentrated to get crystals of pure sugar. People refer to this building as a sugar factory, but it is the beet plant itself that is the *real* sugar factory. In the brick building, workers merely prepare the product of the plant for human use.

Every green-leafed plant is able to get the carbon atoms out of the air's carbon dioxide. And every plant can string these carbon atoms together to make wonderful compounds. But while all plants cannot prepare sugar molecules, all *do* make *cellulose*. From this substance they fashion the fibers out of which stems and wood are formed. In trees, for example, the cellulose forms the trunks, limbs and branches by which a tree lifts and spreads its leaves up into the sunshine.

Why is the tree so "thoughtful" of its leaves? The answer is simple. It is through the leaves — and the vital, green-colored material in them called *chlorophyll* — that the plant gets the carbon atoms it needs for its compound building. The leaves *must have sunshine for this*. A tree crowded by nearby trees will often carry on a race with the others to reach higher into the sunshine it so greatly needs. Even the branches of a single tree will twist out of each other's way as if playing a game of tag.

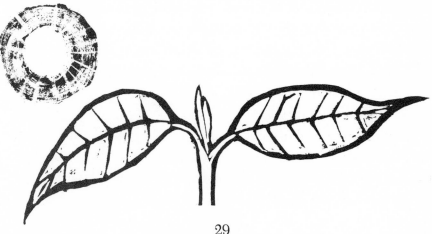

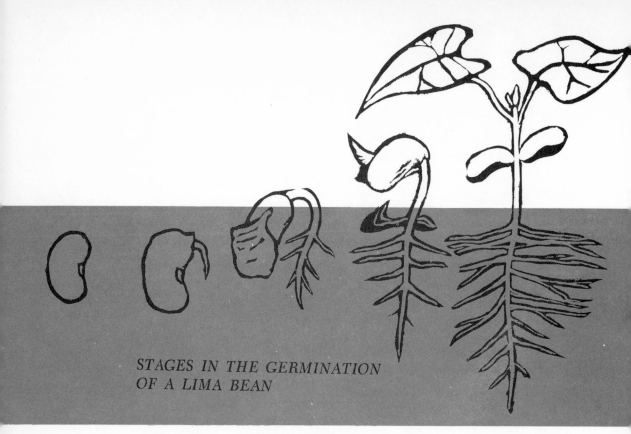

STAGES IN THE GERMINATION
OF A LIMA BEAN

The molecule of chlorophyll is large and intricate. It consists of 55 carbon atoms, 72 hydrogen atoms, 5 oxygen atoms, 4 nitrogen atoms, and one magnesium atom. One might suppose from the bigness of this molecule and its numerous kinds of atoms that only an old plant, "experienced" in stringing atoms together, would be able to handle so many atoms and get them into the right places. But that is not the way of the plant world. Plant a seed in the ground. In time the seed will swell and burst open; a root-part forms that moves *from* the light and a stem-part forms that moves *toward* the light. Reaching the surface of the soil, the sprout soon turns green in the sunshine. The green color is due to chlorophyll. Thus, the little plant — only a day or so old — already "knows" the marvelous way of putting together the carbon, hydrogen, oxygen, nitrogen and magnesium atoms to form chlorophyll. And it will know, too, how to use that substance in getting the carbon atoms out of the air's carbon dioxide.

30

❖13

The Seed Story

To CONTINUE with our story of a plant's growth, we should say something about the chemicals that are packed into the seed. The seed, as it starts into growth in the spring, has to be stuffed with every kind of atom that the young plant will need until it can get food for itself. Actually, these food atoms, in the form of compounds, are already contained in the seed in such a way that they will not soak out when the seeds are caught in a winter rain or snow. But in the spring when the seed starts to grow, it needs its food right away and the material has to be soluble. Therefore, one of the very first things to take place in the bursting seed is the chemical change that produces soluble food materials from those that had previously been insoluble.

Many kinds of plants produce more seeds each year than we might expect would be necessary. And, since each seed is packed with a full assortment of substances needed for growth, the forming of extra seeds would seem to be a drain on the plant's energy. But if we were to examine the matter more fully, we should have to agree that the plants know best. For example, do we see fields of grass dying either because the plants were made too weak by forming too many seeds or because too few seeds were produced to keep the field full of new plants? No, the number of seeds seems just right.

✦14

Another Part of
the Carbon Dioxide Story

ANIMALS, like plants, are wonderful chemists and marvelous builders of complex carbon compounds. But no animal can lie in the sunshine and simply pick carbon atoms out of the air's carbon dioxide molecules. It takes a plant to do that. By eating the plant the animal gets the carbon atoms in a "second-hand" sort of way.

Animals have no need for chlorophyll, so they are not green. They have blood, not sap. In the blood corpuscles is a red colored compound made from atoms of carbon, hydrogen, oxygen, nitrogen and iron called *hemoglobin*. Its part in the activities of the blood is very important. In the lungs the oxygen of the air is on one side of thin membrane walls, while the blood is on the other side. The oxygen molecules enter the blood supply by seeping through the walls. There the hemoglobin chemically picks up the oxygen atoms and the blood moves them rapidly through the body. Any tissues needing oxygen atoms get them from the hemoglobin. The hemoglobin, carried along by the blood, gets back to the lungs for more oxygen atoms. This operation continues over and over again.

Another chemical action is also tied in with the carrying of oxygen by the blood stream. Every time we move a muscle some carbon dioxide (CO_2) is formed. The carbon for it comes from the muscle itself which is a complex carbon compound. The oxygen is supplied by the hemoglobin. This accumulation of carbon dioxide must not be allowed to stay — *it must be moved out of the body*. The blood gets it as far as the lungs, where it seeps out through the membrane walls. Then, in the breathing process, the unwanted CO_2 is expelled into the air.

Whenever we run or jump, a large amout of carbon dioxide will be formed quite suddenly. This sets off a chemical signal. Immediately the heart and chest muscles, acting as a team, go to work to get the carbon dioxide out. The heart beats faster, the blood races along more rapidly, the breathing is hurried up as the chest muscles work harder and faster. Out goes the carbon dioxide. After we rest a while, the heart beat slows down and the breathing is less rapid. This means that the surplus carbon dioxide has been pushed out.

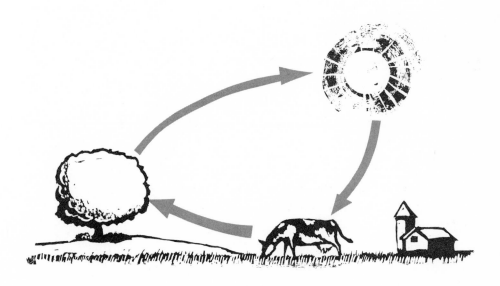

✦ 15

Plastic Legs and Plastic Wings

INSECTS do not have a heart as animals do, nor lungs and chest muscles, nor red blood. One might suppose, then, that their body chemistry would be entirely different from that of animals. While it is true that there are differences, oxygen *is* taken in by insects and carbon dioxide *is* given out — just as in animals.

One important difference in the body chemistry of animals and insects has to do with bones. An animal has them, an insect does not. As an animal grows from a young one to an older one, the bones grow longer and stronger. The muscles attached to the bones grow longer too. But a young insect, like a cicada for example, cannot grow larger as an animal does. Its body is covered with a suit of plastic material that does not stretch very much. To get room for its bigger self as it grows, it makes a bigger plastic suit, partially folded, just inside the old one. Then, when the insect is ready, it splits the back of the old suit and crawls out, swells to take the folds out of the new suit, then rests until the plastic hardens. One of the most interesting things to watch is the way the cicada pulls its plastic-covered feet out of the old plastic suit that has been outgrown. It is not unlike a

34

picture of a cowboy trying to get out of very tight boots!

An even stranger body chemistry is found in the life-cycle of the butterfly. As an insect, it passes through several stages of existence. First, there is the caterpillar stage. Next, comes the chrysalis stage when the body is completely covered by a plastic armor. Finally, the chrysalis cover splits down the back and out comes a gorgeous butterfly. With its small head, bright little eyes, a pair of antennae on its head, and six dainty feet, the newly formed butterfly emerges. The light-weight, beautifully colored wings of plastic have to be inflated and allowed to dry. Then off over the fields it will be ready to go.

What a truly marvelous chemistry this must be that can change a caterpillar to a chrysalis, and a chrysalis to a lovely butterfly.

STAGES IN THE DEVELOPMENT
OF A BUTTERFLY

larvae

egg

caterpillar

chrysalis

butterfly

◈16

Metals, Mountain Men, and Forests

UP TO NOW, we have been discussing the chemistry of living things. But such lifeless things as rocks and minerals have their chemistry, too. Copper atoms may be in the blue or blue-green minerals of the mountains; iron atoms may be in the earth deposits of red-brown hematite; aluminum atoms in the creamy white masses of bauxite.

The story is told that about five thousand years ago some primitive mountain men in the rough, tree-clad hills of western Asia made a strange discovery in the ashes of an old wood fire. Coming back to an open fire-place one day, they pushed the charcoal and half-burned branches from a former fire aside before starting a new fire. A thick seam of bluish-green mineral crossed the surface of the rock and pieces of it, becoming loose, had mingled with the charcoal.

A strong wind happened to be blowing when the new fire was started. In the heat of the roaring wood fire a chemical change took place between the old charcoal and the mineral on the hearth. The mineral contained copper and oxygen atoms; the charcoal was almost entirely made up of carbon atoms. The carbon atoms, drawing away the oxygen atoms to form carbon dioxide molecules, went whirling up with the gases of the wood fire. The copper atoms, left by themselves and clinging together, dropped as molten metal into the ashes below. When the fire was out and the men were ready to leave, they found a lump of copper in a hollow of the hearth. Other mountain men, hearing of their discovery, found that they too could make copper by using charcoal, the bluish-green mineral and a very hot wood fire fanned by the wind. Later they learned how to make a better furnace — one that was covered over with flat rocks and with a chimney at the end where the gases would be carried off by the wind.

Centuries later and in the same part of the world, pellets of iron were found in a hill-side furnace in which a red-brown mineral had been mixed with charcoal. This mineral, now known as *hematite,* is composed of iron and oxygen atoms. The intense heat of the fire had caused the carbon atoms of the charcoal to carry away the oxygen atoms as carbon dioxide, leaving the iron atoms by themselves.

Pure iron is tough; it can be hammered into shape when it is hot but by itself it cannot make hard, sharp-edged tools. However, about three thousand years ago a way was found to change the iron to steel with the aid of charcoal. In this way a hardness came to the iron — and with it a usefulness it had not had before, for steel can be used for sharp-edged tools.

As the centuries passed after this discovery, the production of iron and steel gradually increased. Supplies of iron minerals remained quite large and the forests from which the charcoal was secured were still abundant. In time, however, the situation changed. In the England of a century and a half ago, the forests of oak and beech trees, which made the best charcoal for producing iron, were vanishing. The trees were being cut far faster than new trees could be grown to take their places. The making

COPPER PRODUCING
FURNACE

of iron in England was doomed unless *a substitute for charcoal* could be found.

Coal had been tried in the iron furnaces, but without success. The trouble was not with the carbon, for coal has a great abundance of that. Rather, it came from sulphur atoms present in the coal beds. These worked into the iron and steel being formed — to make them brittle and useless. As soon as the iron workers found that sulphur atoms were the troublemakers, a remedy was found. A good grade of coal was put in a special furnace and heated for a short time by itself. The sulphur atoms escaped as gases. The black, porous solid, called *coke*, that was left was a fine substitute for charcoal in the iron-makers' furnaces.

America is a big country and a busy one. It has iron ore and good coke-producing coal. The production of steel is very great — so great that if it were divided evenly among the people of the entire nation, your share or mine would be about *half a ton of steel a year!*

38

✦17

A Mine in Your Back Yard?

"CLAY is a compound of aluminum. Every clay bank, then, can be looked upon as a mine for a metal that is priced today at several hundred dollars a pound." This surprising statement appeared in a book written about eighty years ago. As a schoolboy in Oberlin, Ohio, Charles Martin Hall read this book. He thought about the statement in the book, dreamed about it, and began making experiments. He experimented when he was in high school, he kept on experimenting when he went to college. In a building in his back yard at home there was a laundry stove. Young Hall got permission to use the building for his private laboratory — "if he was careful."

Using the heat of the stove he tried to get aluminum from the clay he dug up in the yard, employing charcoal as the metal workers did. But the clay merely ended up as brick. Giving up clay, Hall tried bauxite. This mineral is composed of aluminum and oxygen atoms only, and so it seemed an excellent substance to work with. But again Hall got no aluminum. By this time he had become interested in electric batteries and had made several for himself out of glass jars, pieces of zinc and copper, together with some sulphuric acid in the jars. He tried to pass electricity through a lump of bauxite. There was no action. Knowing that electricity will sometimes pass through melted solids better than through unmelted ones, he tried the idea out on bauxite. But the bauxite would not melt. Hall then tried another mineral called *cryolite,* which contains aluminum atoms. He found that he was able to melt it with his stove, but no electricity would pass through the melted material.

Next, almost by accident, he sprinkled some powdered bauxite into the melted cryolite. The bauxite dissolved and disappeared. Connecting up his battery he tried electricity on the melted mixture. Some bubbles appeared at one battery connection. Perhaps he was getting oxygen gas — if so, would he not get aluminum at the other connection? Excitedly, he kept the current on for about an hour. Then, turning it off, he lifted the connection from the liquid. *There were globules of silvery metal — aluminum!* So excited was young Hall that he ran to the college and interrupted classes. Before nightfall, everyone in Oberlin knew that twenty-three-year-old Charles Hall had discovered how to get aluminum by using electricity.

However, to make a real success out of his discovery required several years of careful work and the use of electric current produced by the power plant at Niagara Falls. Thus a light, silvery metal, once priced at two hundred dollars a pound, would soon be produced for about twenty cents a pound. (But no one, as yet, has found a good way to get the aluminum out of clay.)

HALL'S ELECTRICAL ARRANGEMENT

✦18

Living in a Chemical World

IT IS TRUE that in our brief look at chemistry we have not seen a single atom, nor counted the atoms in a single molecule. But we can believe that atoms and molecules do exist. Our *mind* has proved it, not our eyes. And through this new knowledge we should be able to understand things we have been unable to understand before. Picking up a piece of iron or steel we will realize that men have made these metals out of iron minerals from the earth and through the use of charcoal or coke. We will realize too that the metals will go back to rust unless we, or others, care for them correctly.

Moreover, in our new knowledge we can realize that we are not mere observers in a chemical world but that we are — and should be — active partners in it. As we walk across the fields, through the orchards and beside the berry patches toward the forest edge, we are aware that the plants about us are busy preparing new compounds in their noiseless chemical factories. As we watch the feeding cattle and the butterflies drifting from blossom to blossom we can marvel at the strange and wonderful chemical ways of life.

We have said little about ourselves in this book. Yet there is much that could be said. Our body parts are working as a marvelous chemical team in everything we do. Tonight we can sleep peacefully, knowing that our chemical team has controls that will wake us, as usual, with the new day.

A table of 40 common or important elements, with the letter symbols for the atoms

Name	Symbol	Name	Symbol
aluminum	Al	lithium	Li
argon	A	magnesium	Mg
barium	Ba	manganese	Mn
beryllium	Be	mercury	Hg
bismuth	Bi	neon	Ne
boron	B	nickel	Ni
bromine	Br	nitrogen	N
cadmium	Cd	oxygen	O
calcium	Ca	phosphorus	P
carbon	C	platinum	Pt
chlorine	Cl	potassium	K
chromium	Cr	radium	Ra
copper	Cu	silicon	Si
fluorine	F	silver	Ag
gold	Au	sodium	Na
helium	He	strontium	Sr
hydrogen	H	sulphur (sulfur)	S
iodine	I	tin	Sn
iron	Fe	uranium	U
lead	Pb	zinc	Zn

Materials and supplies for use in experiments

General materials from the home
    Aluminum foil, and an-aluminum-foil pan
    Watercolor brush
    A bright clean nail
    A wad of clean steel wool (free from soap)
    A magnet
    Paper toweling
    An empty pop bottle
    Two paper cups of same size
    A yardstick or slender lath two to three feet long
    A pencil having six sides
    A birthday candle and a large candle
    A drinking straw

Chemical substances from the home
    The juice of a lemon
    A teaspoonful of sugar
    A bottle of purple grape juice or a can of blackberries
    Two fluid ounces of vinegar
    Baking soda
    Borax, or a piece of soap

Substances from the drug store
    Half a spoonful of blue vitriol crystals
    A bottle with a cap to keep the crystals in
    4 fluid ounces of clear limewater in stoppered bottle
    A cork to fit the pop bottle
    A few green vitriol crystals

Index

47

M

Magnetism, and iron rust, 4
Marsh gas (methane), 22-26
Materials, for experiments (list), 45
Messages, secret, 3
Metals, 36-38
Methane (marsh gas), 22-26
Methanol, 27
Methyl butyrate, 12
Methyl salicylate, 13
Mint leaves, odor of, 13
Molecules, 6-7

N

Natural gas, *see* Methane
Nitrogen, in air, 16-17

O

Oberlin College, Ohio, 39-40
Octyl acetate, 13
Odors, 12-13
Oil of wintergreen, 13
Oxidation, 4-5
Oxygen:
    in air, 16-17
    in breathing process, 32-33
    in iron rust, 4-5

P

Paraffin, chemicals in, 24
Peaches, odor of, 12
Peppermint, odor of, 13
Photosynthesis, 27-31
Pine trees, odor of, 13
Pineapples, odor of, 12-13
Plant growth, 27-31
Plant oils, 12-13

R

Ripeness, in fruits, 14-15
Rust, 4-5

S

Salicylates, 13
Secret messages, 3
Seeds, 30-31
Smells, 12-13
Soapy water, as an antiacid, 14
Steel, 37-38
Steel wool, in experiments, 1, 4, 11
Sugar, 1-2, 7-8
Sugar beets, 28-29
Sugar molecule, 7, 28
Sulphur, in steel, 38
Sunshine, need of plants for, 29
Supplies, for experiments (list), 45

V

Van Helmont, Jan, 17-19
Vanilla, 13
Vanillin, 13
Vaporization, 16
Vinegar, as an acid, 14
Vinegar-baking soda experiment, 17-19

W

Washington, George, 23
Water molecules, 6-7
Wintergreen berries, odor of, 13
Wood, chemically changed by heat, 27
Wood tar, 27
Wood vinegar, 27